NO LOVE R.

No Love Rations

& Other Stories

TOM KELLY

Postbox
PRESS

First published in 2022 by Postbox Press,
the literary fiction imprint of Red Squirrel Press
36 Elphinstone Crescent
Biggar
South Lanarkshire
ML12 6GU
www.redsquirelpress.com

Edited by Colin Will

Layout, design and typesetting by Gerry Cambridge
gerry.cambridge@btinternet.com

Cover artwork: Nata Bene/shutterstock.com

A CIP catalogue record for this book is available
from the British Library.

ISBN: 978 1 913632 33 5

Red Squirrel Press and Postbox Press are committed
to a sustainable future. This publication is printed in
the UK by Imprint Digital using Forest Stewardship
Council certified paper.
www.digital.imprint.co.uk

• *Contents* •

• *Welcome Stranger* •

LYING ON THE PAVEMENT, sun burns peach cheeks—at night I watch streetlight semaphore me as older children run dizzyingly around the fading green lamp post. I yearn to lap with them. My sister sleeps. The radio in the next room tells mam and dad of some mystery I can only guess at. I cling onto my bed clothes as sleep slides in, like a welcome stranger.

• *Christmas Eve, Hope Street, Jarrow* •

I KEEP GOING BACK to the same two rooms with the dying widow below and darkness that eats me. It is Christmas Eve with the smell of snow in the air. There is an ominous muffled thud from below. I slip deeper into the bed awaiting his visit feigning sleep. Mother's anxious voice hissed in the dark, 'You'll have to come downstairs with me, your dad can't.' Dad couldn't, he had an accident in the shipyard a few weeks earlier, 'Left his toes in his boot', someone cryptically said.

Creaking down wooden stairs, cold bit me stomach. An early Christmas present, a bicycle torch, led the way, dancing down the stairs and diving to the ceiling. The key skated across the barrel before connecting and the torch eventually settled on the widow's cream mask face which faced the floor. She was dead.

The rest was formality, women in the street would 'lay her out.' The identity of Santa Claus forgotten in light of more pressing matters.

• *Swim Out of Me Dream* •

AA'M TRAWLING STREETS, aa shiny armband of hard snot on me sleeve, watching aa green bubble frogspawn from me mates' nose. It's that time of day or night when th' sky's closing in, been booted ti' bits, looks nearly dead, not bright as aa button it was first thing this dawning.

Me mother's hanging out th' washing in the back-yard, pegging upside down clothes that should by rights vomit on th' star-struck concrete but don't, th' just billow tunnels of nowt.

Dad's at work. Aa see him nights when dark starts. He smells of factory. Aa word aa get me tongue round with no idea what it means. Granda's in th' shipyard, at th' back of ower street. He walks home with a pipe fixed in his mouth, aa small spear leaving smoke winging behind him. Aa'm here, look up at th' window, ye can just see me behind th' curtain lifting with th' draft.

Dead heavy dark sits on me head and sometimes aa can't sleep; it's too cold or too hot an' anyway th' story on the radio was scary but looking at me comic in th' dark will save me. It's still hard t' sleep, me eyes flutter an' aa try to not get into th' dream aa don't want.

Aa'm drowning, an' pulled by th' hair out of th' swimming baths, th' pebble edge cutting into me skin as aa'm dragged ti' th' side, spewing onto th'

unforgiving pool-side. Me bedroom smells of chlo-
rine, an' aa push out me arms when aa swim out of
me dream.

• *The Day Rationing Ended* •

I AM WITH MY UNCLE TOMMY, red-faced, garrulous, as my head just reaches above the table outside the pub. I eye a pint big as a bucket. Uncle lets me sup his beer and laughs so hard at my reaction I think he will die. He fought in Burma. I am sorry I did not hear his World War Two stories. My mam's brother is loved by everyone. He must have been baby-sitting me and had to go to a pub. He was at home there.

The pub's nickname, 'The Spike,' is where men would break-up rocks used as hardcore on roads. They were paid a few shillings a day. My Granda Kelly included. Look closely, we are all there, breaking-up rocks, having a pint and me as a child, spitting out the bitter beer. Standing where the pub stood eyeing the Slake or Slaaks, as it is known, which is narrower than I remember. Gone are the vivid colours gifted by the chemical works.

I walk to the Co-op Undertakers, they made coffins on High Street. Standing at the door a life-time later see me watching the boy I was, wanting a bag of sawdust for my rabbits. Listen to the high-pitched yell, a man concentrates, gimlet eyes lost in dust. I am holding an empty sack, having it filled for my rabbits to piss and leave small cannon balls of shit.

There is a thick as a bull's lug navy blue coat at the bottom of my bed. I pull it up and smell the cold. Snow is tickling the window pane. Sliding further down the bed I listen to the rest of the world as if my life depended upon it. The shipyard is alive with riveters' hammers serenading from what amounts to a few streets and a bar away. The world, I discover a life-time later, is changing. I handle the cold and look out the window and push it open and hear the yard drumming. Tonight, I do that. I am that child.

Around the back of our house there is demolition, imagine a war-torn city. I do not know that tomorrow mam will scream as blood circles into my mouth. Tonight, the sky is lumpen with snow and I imagine swirling around in its blue-greyness. The street light flickers but not before capturing a man and woman kissing as if their life depended upon it. If I tell mam she will demand more information. I dare not say. I promise myself to be silent. I excuse myself by saying it was only a kiss.

I sit for hours seeing the night take shape. Snow has a solitary man bowing in supplication to the wind after a few pints in the *Duke of Wellington*. A group of men smell of the shipyard as they laugh and spit their way home. A family return from the 'first house' at the pictures. They are happy and cling together, a huddle making me break into a smile I take back to bed with me.

The next day playing upstairs in a house being demolished I look down, and see the floor downstairs. I am standing on floorboards quickly becoming fewer. I picture myself falling. Sweat gathers and runs into my eyes, having me blink as I stick my head out a window and shout, 'Don't throw any more stones'. I am too late and catch the last stone on my brow and blood gathers into my helpless hands. Mam is told of the accident and drags me to Palmers Hospital. Now I feel the mark on my brow and remember the day rationing ended.

· *John Wayne and Me* ·

THE SUITCASE IS THE FIRST step on the road back to mam and dad. I can see us sitting side-by-side. The radio crackling with *Two-Way Family Favourites* as I wait for dad to open his suitcase while they singalong to Dean Martin: I am so pleased none of my friends can hear them singing, 'The sweet, sweet, the memories you gave a-me, you can't beat the memories you gave a-me...' Dad said to me, 'We're lovely singers, aren't we?' Mam was aware of my face-ache, 'He doesn't like us singing. He's more interested in your suitcase.' Mam knew what I wanted, 'Howay dad let's have aa look. Will ye give me ya medals dad? When aa'm old, dead old, like seventeen. What's in that wooden box?' Mam showed her anxiety, 'I wish you would get rid of it. It'll end in tears.' Dad said, 'Don't talk daft.'

I can see Dad holding his Green Howard's cap badge. There's a photograph of me wearing it and has me stepping back to the moment it was taken. Standing against a wall, the school photographer lining us up, the quick click and away, there were forty-odd in my class, there wouldn't be a lot of time. We didn't have a camera at home, so it's difficult, sometimes, to put yourself in time and place but this photograph does just that. I had cut my hair and made an inverted V at the front. And there is my dad's Green Howards cap badge on my jacket's lapel. I wanted to be a soldier. I would march up and down in the kitchen with dad shouting out instructions, 'Stand tall. Swing your arms. Not both together. Where's your rifle? You'll be on a charge boy. Stand to attention.'

Standing tall and proud as any soldier marching with a poker but it was a real gun to me and I'd kill the enemy. My heart was bursting with pride. I had to be brave, just like dad. I pressed dad about his war, 'Will aa fight in aa war like you?' Dad turned serious, 'I hope to God you don't have to. Aa saw enough for the both of us.'

Mam went to the shops and with her out of the house, dad would continue with his story as I filled in the details: that was our routine. I had heard the stories dozens of times but wouldn't let him miss anything out. Dad battled on, 'We were parachuted into Norway in April 1940 and ended-up in a village called...'

I dived in, 'Voss.'

'That's right son, near Stavanger...'

I jumped in again, 'Aa bet it was great.'

Dad turned away from me and seemed to be looking for something in the backyard before he spoke, 'War's not glorious son. Ask your uncle Tommy, he'll tell you it was no picnic in Burma and your uncle John ended-up in a Japanese prisoner-of-war camp.'

It was glorious to me. You didn't die. You would wake up next day, go to school, play football. Death wasn't forever. I put dad's medals in a line across my chest and pinned the cap badge on my balaclava, praying mam wouldn't come back before dad opened that wooden box. Dad went on as I sat at his feet, 'So, we were parachuted into Norway but the Germans outnumbered us, it was a hell of a battle and we had to retreat... we lost a lot of lads...'

Dad was talking slowly as I said, 'What's in your eye dad? Use me hankie, it's nearly clean.' Dad seemed angry as I watched his face turn stern, 'It's not like in your comics, you don't play with bits of wood, they're real guns and bullets and when you fall down dead you don't get up.'

In the *History of The Green Howards*, it says: 'The Green Howards conducted an adventurous withdrawal through the mountains by train, truck and foot and on April 30th, 1940, the navy took off the ravenously hungry survivors by the light of the bombed and burning Norwegian villages. The Brigade had performed a classic withdrawal operation'.

'Classic withdrawal?' Dad was captured by the Germans, 'The first words of German aa heard were "Achtung". We'd been led into a trap, by a quisling. He said he'd take us to Sweden which was a neutral country. We were in a mountain hut and the Germans surrounded us and then took us ti' Poland and had us working on farms all the way there. Me mam and dad thought aa was dead and...'

The newspaper cutting was in my hand, 'I know what happened next dad, you were in the paper and they read out your name on the wireless...' Dad read from the newspaper cutting, 'Among the list of British prisoners broadcast from Hamburg last night....'

'It was you dad.'

Dad smiled, 'Aye me mam and dad thought aa was dead until Lord Haw Haw gave me name out on the radio.'

I wanted more of the story, 'Tell us about Poland and the camps.' Dad picked up his war medals and spoke with heart-stopping emotion, 'The Polish people treated us well, aa remember finding a loaf of bread left for me under a barrow by the farm workers, they had nowt but they still gave us. And aa remember queuing up in the camp for soup and me and me mate could see there wasn't going to be enough, so we got a bowl of hot water and threw it in the faces of other lads in the queue and grabbed our share. If ye didn't ye'd die, it was dog-eat-dog. Aa'm not proud of that but aa wouldn't be here if aa hadn't done it.' Five years in a prison-of-war camp. The scars stayed with him all his life.

Mam came back from shopping and caught us by surprise, 'Come on you two. Move yourselves. Aa've told you, get rid of that box.' And that was the end of dad telling his war stories. I sat reading my comic but all I wanted to do more than anything in the entire world was open the box in dad's suitcase.

There was a time-bomb under my parents' bed. In the coal black night under the hissing gas mantle something was burning through me but it was our night at the *Regal*, for the weekly ritual of worshipping celluloid Gods on the magic screen.

We walked to the pictures, our voices converging,

'What's on mam?'

'Operation Pacific,' was mam's quick reply.

Dad added, 'How John Wayne won the war.'

I said, 'Dad, dad, did you know John Wayne?'

Mam laughed, 'After a few pints your dad's met them all.'

In the pictures, war was glorious. Nobody died, they lived forever, safe and secure with their mams and dads. Then I heard me mam's angry tight-lipped whisper, like enemy gun fire spitting out of the dark, 'If you don't get rid of it, it'll go in the Tyne.' I wondered what was going to be thrown in the river? Next doors cat? Mam hated it. I knew it had made a mess in our house, but that seemed drastic. I wondered if it was the rabbits? We used to breed them and I would bump into one or two dancing a dead dance on the backyard clothes line, generally after dad had met somebody in a pub who fancied a rabbit pie. Maybe mam wanted rid of them, she had more than enough of their smell and those little brown marbles piling up in the straw.

Walking home from the pictures it hit me, 'The wooden box.' I would never discover what was in it. The Holy Grail was so near in our bedroom, under mam and dad's bed. I felt like a proper soldier, when somebody needs saving from the jaws of death, like John Wayne winning the war, but now I had my own battle: What could I do?

The only thing on my mind was the wooden box. I sat with the *Eagle* comic glued to my face but I wasn't reading. I was thinking and planning. The next night mam pulled a funny face and said, 'Can you hear squeaking?' Dad was reading *The Daily Herald* but eventually did answer, 'That'll be the mice.' Mam screamed, 'Mice?' Dad was still reading and answered from behind the paper, 'Aa see them first thing in the morning, just before aa go to work. Aa gave them aa bit breakfast. They play lovely in the hearth; they're living in the couch.' Mam's voice went up several octaves, 'Why didn't ye say?' Dad reluctantly put down the paper, 'You're always asleep in the morning.' Mam was red in the face. I nearly said something about her looking like a clown but didn't as she let out a yell, 'They're underneath us?' Dad was now taking notice, 'Take it easy, the neighbours will think aa'm murdering you.' I thought she was really going to kill dad as she screamed, 'Aa'll kill you.' I decided to join in, 'Aa can hear them mam, squeak, squeak.' Mam was near the door and pointed at dad, as if she was going to spear him. She said slowly, 'Get them out now.'

Dad was still sitting in his chair when he said, 'Wait until after me tea.' Mam had the door wide-open; a cold draught ran into the house, 'There'll be no tea 'til you get rid of those mice. Aa mean it. The bairn'll give you aa hand to take the couch into the back yard.' Dad and me fought with the couch down the wooden stairs into the backyard, the mice were screaming but mam was screaming even louder. The whole street must have heard her, 'Get them out. It's a nightmare. Mice living under us. Mice. I hate mice. Keep them out of the toilet and shut the coal house door.' Dad, in a matter-fact way said to me, 'Hand me that knife.' I thought he was going to slice their heads off. I was preparing myself for a lot of blood. Mam screamed. Dad slit the underside of the couch; it was like killing an animal, spilling its intestines and white pink-eyed mice ran into the backyard, dozens and dozens of them squealed and squinted into the light. Mam screamed again. We attacked them, me with a shovel, dad with a hammer. They ran for the drain as we chased and battered and battered them: it was exciting. I was killing the enemy: the mice. We gathered the mice together, scraping their dead bodies along the backyard, leaving a film of blood, half bits of legs and heads in a terrible trail. I didn't think. I just did it.

My mam watched from upstairs, standing behind the net curtain like a failure, a flag of truce but not for us, we had won. We had defeated them; it was John Wayne and me. I was glorious in battle. Dad shouted up to mam, standing upstairs, away from the carnage, 'They're dead, well and truly dead.' I can see the white and pink carpet of dead mice dumped in the bottom of the dustbin. Dad put his arm around me as if we had done something great together. I felt like a hero and wanted more, much more than that cushion of white mice with blood speckled over them, like monkeys' blood you get on ice-cream, except this was real. This blood was dead real. I looked up to dad who was wiping the blood from his hands on the wall. I said, 'Dad, was aa good help?' He looked down at me and smiled, 'You wor aa proper little soldier.'

As I washed my hands in the water bucket and started getting ready for church; after the killings, I knew I had to open the box and felt strange but excited. The priest was on the altar with a golden cross embroidered on the back of his vestments, I was at Mass but in a different world. The priest would never kill mice because he was God's messenger on Earth and could send me to Hell. My knees were dead as I kneeled but couldn't pray, instead I went over the battle with the mice. No 'Last Post' for them, no six-gun salute, no being saved by Flash Gordon, just the realness of death. I felt a shiver which had me scared and got my handkerchief back from dad. God was not blessing our killing. I was worried. There was a tight knot in my stomach that would not go away.

As we walked home from church to the scene of our crime, the fight, battle, killings, my eight-year-old self was struggling to come to terms with life and death. I felt nervous and said, 'Aa want to go to the toilet.' And began to run home. As I ran, telling myself, 'Aa've got to open the box'. I fumbled with the door key. Mam and dad were at the top of the street, I dragged the suitcase from underneath the bed and threw it open, 'Aa gun.'

My heart was drumming like a terrified bird. I began to sweat and could hardly breathe. I dashed into my room and put the gun under my pillow. Now I knew what was in the wooden box and needed time to compose myself and dwell on the power of the gun that would lie under my head tonight. I had killed mice and now I had a gun. I would be John Wayne and could not stop shivering with excitement. All the time thinking about the weight of the gun and my stomach gurgled. I felt sick as I tried to think of a plan.

In my bedroom I embraced my pillow as the gun nestled and burned against my cheek and it was so heavy. I felt it in the dark. Mam came into the room. My finger was stroking the trigger. She left the room and shut the door. I got a shock and squeezed the trigger. It was pointed at the door. Everything stood perfectly still, like a photograph, as if it wasn't real and the loudest bang in the world rang round the bedroom. I could hear my dad scream.

Dad had kept the gun from the army and mam was always telling him to get rid of it. The ambulance and police came. All of the street stared at our house. And later there was an inquest but they could not charge a child of eight with killing his mother. 'A tragic accident,' they said.

• *Confession* •

I SPENT A LOT OF THE TIME looking into the coal fire, thinking of the flames of Hell, that's the sort of thing a Catholic boy does. You imagine burning forever. I would say to myself, 'It must be right; otherwise, why would the priest tell ye. It has to be true.' Mam, dad and my sister are here somewhere. Was I afraid? Terrified? Take your pick. Make a choice. Throw a dart. Win a coconut. Hope is in the air. The future is big. Over there behind the *Duke of Wellington* bar, is the coaly Tyne, the shipyards, with boats on their way to everywhere in the world. We lived in Hope Street. And as the song says, 'We had high hopes!' And the power of prayer, 'Our Father who art in Heaven hallowed be thy name...'

I feel God's grace and see Christ bleeding on his cross walking to Mass. We walk down Salem Street to St Bede's Church where God's held in a golden cage, with a light shining forever; that's how I saw and felt it. The Holy Ghost found me but I didn't say. I kept it to myself. He came through our window, hovered round the floating white net, drifting above my bed and threw burning coals which see-sawed round the room. It was not a dream. The coals were blood red with streaks of gold, like bloodlines in rocks. God was placing blood into me, 'God made me to know him and love and serve him in this world and to be happy with him forever in the next.' The 'next,' the other life was real. I stood at my window looking at the street. A gas lamp was outside our window, its flame whispering. A foreign seaman walked up the street, then knocked on a door. There was a prostitute in our street; not a proper one you see with fur coats and no knickers outside the dock, she was an enthusiastic amateur. 'Did it for cigarettes and stockings', I heard dad say. A new man every week with different tattoos, one of them gave me a bar of chocolate, the biggest I had ever seen.

I spun nights away around the blue-green lamppost and played football, with dad on the field: it was a religious experience. Night cut in and all you could see were our grey ghosts kicking an almost invisible ball, back and forward on a hidden and magic piece of elastic. The ball becoming rosary beads passing between us, 'Out of the depths I cry to thee oh Lord, Lord hear my prayers...' And he did. He listened as I prayed with such intensity when man and dad shuffled in their bed, moaned in pretend sleep as I lay wide-eyed staring into the black night. We all slept in one room. Mam, dad, my sister and me. Three beds, a wardrobe, chest of drawers beside the window and no room for anything else. I could hear the ships stealing in and out of the Tyne, near-silent burglars in the petrol blackness. The Shell Mex depot rattled with trucks and at eight-and-three quarters I was washed away in this world. I didn't know anything, I just felt it.

Saturday night was the time you got rid of your

sins at Confession. Not that I had many, lots of venial sins, no mortal ones. Mortal sins meant you would go straight to Hell forever. 'Forever' was a worry. How long was it? If you didn't confess and if you happened to be knocked down by the number 69 bus you would go to Hell, for all eternity, mortal sins weighed you down. I kneeled in the Confessional Box, 'Bless me father for I have sinned, it is one week since my last Confession...'

I would tell my sins, seeing the outline of the priest behind his grill. He was whispering and praying and said to me, 'Say three Hail Marys and make an Act of Contrition.'

This was my life: I believed implicitly in the power of prayer. If I died with a mortal sin on my soul, I would go straight to Hell. See me sitting by the fire, watching the flames lap up the chimney: the flames of Hell and me burning forever. Confession saved my soul.

• *The Hen Cree* •

IT IS AUGUST 1956. I am nine-years-old and at Granda and Granny's. Granda's boots are warming before the specially prepared to last-for-a-day coal fire, flanked *by grey faceless sentries of socks,* they were very poetic socks. Rosemary Clooney's on the radio, 'Hey mambo, mambo Italiano, Hey mambo mambo Italiano...' I sat on the edge of a chair seriously observing Granda as he smoked his pipe with a smack and spat in the fire. Maggie, my Granny, screamed as the sizzling saliva broke through her deafness, 'What have aa told ye!? Cut that out.' Without looking up Granda grunted, 'It's only spit.'

He initially ignored Granny getting ready. She wore a black coat and produced, from a cardboard box, a pink luminous hat. He looked incredulously and said, 'There's no chance ye'll not be seen.' Granda, again without turning to Granny said, 'De ye want aa trowel to shovel on any more of that rouge? Ye've got me choked.' She continued to squint at the distorted mirror and replied out of the side of her mouth, 'Aa'll choke you.' She studiously ignored him as she told me, 'I'll leave the lights on, ye can't be too careful, it'll make the burglars think we're in.' Granda, ever the realist, replied, 'Ye've got the curtains closed. No bugger will see we've got the bloody lights on.'

We began our journey to Uncle Jimmy's caravan,

an eternity away, outside Newcastle. It was raining. Granda muttered as we headed for the bus, 'Jimmy's only been away three days...it's belted down every day...cats and dogs...like bloody stair rods...never bloody stopped...bloody hell.' Granny looked closely at me and said, 'They'll appreciate us making the effort.' She then fell silent for an age.

I got used to Granny and Granda's silence. It was part of them, the silence and the looks on the bus to Newcastle as Granny's hat began to weep; pink dye tinting her grey hair. She said, more in hope, 'Our Jimmy won't be far away today' as we floated through Gateshead. Leaving the bus, we ploughed into the rain bubbling out of the ground as birds flapped into hiding.

Granny with hope in her voice said, 'It'll ease off...it's just aa shower...ye'll see...' Granda pulled down his flat cap and began a litany of watery images, 'The bloody ducks have umbrellas...it's never stopped woman.' He was cut short by an angry look from Grandma. The trek from Worswick Street bus station to Newcastle Central Station was memorable; Granda sulking and sodden walked ten yards ahead of us. We shuffled on and couldn't lift our sodden heads in the torrential rain.

The hat was now lying at right angles on Granny's sodden head and the area where her hat had vacated, a bright semi-circle of pink: People began to notice. She was agitated and spat out at Granda, 'Aa know ye don't want to be here...make an effort... don't be so selfish...'

Wringing out his cap he spat out, 'Aa wish aa was aa shell fish. This is bloody ridiculous...wa soaked to the skin...you look like a bloody clown...and the bairn is like an orphan in the storm.' I wondered why I was an *orphan in the storm* but didn't say.

The pillars of Central Station were a welcome sight, we sheltered like frozen holidaymakers in sea front chalets. Trains *wheezed, leaning wearily against the platform before thudding into life*. We had poetic trains. There was an hour to wait for our train and we sat in the Station Buffet. Granny forced out a smile, 'it's nice in here.' Granda jumped in with, '*Nicer* than where?' Granny gave an exaggerated smile to the waitress, 'Three cups of tea please, wa going to see our son and his family...in a caravan... at Ovingham...yes...pity about the weather.... No, he's not called 'Noah.' Granda drank his tea and pulled a face and moaned, 'This tastes like gnats pi...' Granny's look was enough to silence him as she adjusted her hat exposing a new show of pink. A tall woman, who picked her nose previously, smiled to her friend, and in unison they looked towards my Granny's head. I followed their smug eyes. *Smug eyes*: I recognized a good line even at nine. Granny dived into a series of mutters, 'Your Granda'll say the train's too slow...too noisy...he didn't want to leave the house where he can back his horses... donkeys more like.'

On the train we had a carriage to ourselves and sat silent and dripping the entire journey. Listening to the rain drumming against the windows I almost fell asleep but waited instead for a tunnel to catch grandfather's stony reflection in the window and said, 'This is like aa propa holiday...'

Granny, looking at Granda replied, 'Me first in years...'

Granda grumbled, 'First and bloody last.'

She turned and pointedly replied to me, 'Aa'm always saying to your Granda, let's go down to Shields...so aa can dangle me feet off the Pier.'

Granda, looking away said, 'Ye'd have to have bloody long legs.'

Leaving the train, she ignored him, 'There's aa bus to the caravan site...'

Granda, wringing out his cap again, said, 'We must be near bloody Timbuktu.'

It was five monsoon minutes to the caravan site. *Monsoon minutes?* Poetic trains and now it was the weather. My trousers were sticking to my legs. I said to Granny, 'Ye'd think aa've wet meself.' Ignoring me she pointed at a 'This way to the caravan site' sign.

Rain cascaded into our shoes. Granny almost screamed with delight, 'Jimmy and the bairns will be glad to see us...'

Granda gave us a rain-check ,'Feet are bloody soaking...This'll be the death of me...what aa bloody day... Aa've had aa better time in the Chapel of Rest...'

Granny gave him one of her looks, and spat out, 'Don't tempt me to say anything. Not in front of the bairn.' He dropped his cap, picked it up, wrung it into a tight ball and just then began to slip like someone losing their footing on an ice rink: he eventually fell. His voice became a snarl, 'That's me finished...aa'm soaked to the skin...me bloody socks and trousers....bloody hell.' Granda fell again.

Granny almost screeched, 'That's ye wickedness coming out...ye've been aa pain...aa right pain and now you're paying for it...there is aa God in Heaven ...that's what you get for ya wickedness...'

There was a gravel path into the field where the caravans were moored. Granny's hat had become smaller and her shoulders were daubed with pink. She gave Granda a warning, 'Watch out for the cow...muck...it's everywhere...aa ye listening? Be careful...aa said be care...' Granda slipped again and fell into the cow dung. He stooped down to get his cap. Granny warned him again, 'That's not your cap! It's cow...' His trousers were *blessed with brown*. We were at Uncle Jimmy's caravan and Granda shouted, 'It's aa bloody hen cree.'

A caravan neighbour broke the news, 'They left on Wednesday, the weather you know.' Granda threw down his hat and Granny followed suit by throwing her pink hat to the ground. We padded wearily home as, on cue, it began to thunder.

• *Seeing the Light* •

WE HAD ELECTRICITY in our newly built Council house. No more gas mantles muttering animal noises after we pulled the metal chain, woo-oofing into blue — then cream — light. On reflection creating light was an art.

I thought everything would be easier, better for all of us in the late 1950s, but my childhood ended when we left our jerry-built upstairs flat by the river. The light switch confirmed that. All we had to do was press a switch. I thought, glibly, that the dark would be the same, but doubt crept into my every uneasy dream.

• *At Eleven* •

I SAW MY FIRST DEAD BODY. See me, a quiet altar boy keeping close to the priest. Street lights reveal a veneer of frost on pavements but hid the door numbers in the search for the deceased's home. Winter light disappeared as we headed up the shadeless stair-head, making me feel uneasy, exposed.

When the priest entered the bedroom, murmuring conversation died. There was a silence you could taste. The sweat on the priest's brow slowly fell into his eyes and I heard his stomach rumble because of the tea he had been forced to miss; he had whispered this to me as we bundled out of his car.

The priest must have been used to quiet rooms. He handed me his thick dark and heavy overcoat; I was unsure what to do with the coat and left it folded over my arms, feeling like a soldier on guard duty. The unnerving silence continued for an eternity. The mourners were in an almond-shape and broke-up to allow the priest to stand at the apex as he pulled over his head a white embroidered halter he kissed and placed around his neck. Decade-after-decade of the rosary began, 'Hail Mary, full of grace...' The call and response was hypnotic and transcendental as I secretly examined each face, their eyes drawn to the coffin to the dead man I knew.

I need to picture and smell the room. I have not given the priest a clear image. His dark curly hair sprang over his brow like a broken cartwheel. I see him now as a man doing his job, no vocation, giving comfort to these people gathered together through grief and obligation.

To me all the mourners were ancient: death was for the very old. Yet I felt uncertain realising I knew the man. He was a friend of my dad. Did this mean dad would be joining him soon? I tried not to look at him closely but his stillness drew me to him. He was clean-shaven and I could see a shadow running along his jaw to a broad, dimpled chin.

Going back to this home now makes me realise it was his bedroom. Their children praying were all too aware of that. What must they have felt? The carpet was damp. The bedding ironed. He had slept here but now, 'He's on his last sleep', my Granny would have said. His coffin levitated above metal supports, provided by the undertaker, who brought the body home while his wife prepared for his sad return.

HE WAS A BROTHER of the Church who went around the parish visiting the elderly and infirm. I tagged along listening to tales of how life was too brief and the past was nothing short of golden. I said little. What could I add? Twelve-years-old, wearing a jacket with see-through elbows and trousers that fitted me a year or two previously. My clothes, like the parishioners', had seen better days. The Brother of the Church was stoic. He listened. This is what people seemed to crave.

One couple were different. The man had been a Headmaster. He stood ram-rod-like and every part of him seemed as if it had been pressed by a very heavy iron. For whatever reason, he did not smile. His wife was stooped and said little, but did smile as if to compensate for her husband's inability in the smiling stakes.

The Headmaster was revered by my dad. I visited this couple on a number of occasions and each time closely examined the unsmiling and incredibly 'ironed man' for reasons why my dad thought so highly of him. My mother, who could be cruel and extremely funny when diagnosing anyone, said nothing of the 'ironed man.' It was a secret she saved. Each visit became, for me, an examination, 'What did he talk about?' Dad would say. A few words of our conversation seemed to satisfy his thirst. He asked if he ever spoke of him. My answers were brevity itself. Generally, of the 'yes' and 'no' variety. I must, however, have sated his desire for knowledge as he headed to the bar with a broad smile.

I would sit in the 'ironed man's' council bungalow feeling I knew the word 'council' intimately as it was one of the few the wife repeated. She said it looking to her husband and that was the only occasion he would remain silent. He side-stepped her glance deftly as Fred Astaire, telling us of college days. The Brother of the Church smiled and looked towards me and I felt we had shared a secret handshake. We were allowing this man to rejoice in his past. I told my dad the story of his rise to become Headmaster: the opponents, a priest who preferred another candidate and eventual victory. At the end of the story, with legs apart, he was king of this particular castle smiling for nothing short of eternity.

His reverie was cut short by his wife telling a brutal story with a smile, ending with the harsh words, 'And now will you tell why the Headmaster and dear wife ended up in a council bungalow that is so small we have had to sell all but what we stood up in?' As she spoke small red patches appeared on her cheeks. The rouge she used to give her pallid face some colour could not disguise the stigmata of anger. Perspiration deftly followed the contours of steely grey hair. She surprised me by moving quickly round the room, not once looking at her husband, who now sat silently on the high-backed chair. He did not move as his eyes bore into the heavy curtains; I noticed for the first time they were too long and lapped along the thread-bare carpet.

We were judge and jury, this was her summing-up speech. Words she must have garnered over years, vitriol dripped from her now thin lips. I was embarrassed. Sweat ran slowly down my red face. I did not move. She went on and on.

Her husband's anger was tangible yet was stuck in his throat. Suffocating hostility like a bad smell pervaded the room. I began to capture her words as if they were printed on the dark heavy curtains. The Headmaster had invested all their savings and pension fund into stocks and shares. A man had advised him. Her husband was impressed. She described him. His movie star moustache, blue pin-striped suit and love of 'flowery language.' She underlined this phrase scornfully. Language, with quotes from Shakespeare, won over the Headmaster. Money was transferred to the 'quoting man's' bank account. The man disappeared as did all their savings.

The red mark on her cheeks retreated. He stood up slowly. The Brother of the Church nodded to me. We began to leave this domestic storm. The atmosphere was akin to a melancholic Angelus Bell. I didn't tell the story when dad left for the 'ironed man's' funeral, when I saw him cry for the first time and had me so upset, I held a knuckle in my mouth, not wanting anyone to hear my sobs in our ice-cold toilet.

My mother told me she knew the Headmaster's

story. She thought it best to stay silent. And added, 'ignorance is bliss.' After the funeral, when dad left for the bar, she held my arm tightly, smiling through near-clenched teeth saying, 'I have not told your dad. It would break his heart.' She made me promise never to tell him.

I remained silent that day and it is only now with dad dead all these years that I tell the tale of the 'Ironed Man,' without hurting him: something I would never do.

• *Pot of Gold* •

GRANNY IS SEARCHING in the coal fire. Flames flutter through the cast iron grate as smoke signals rise. I watch her face with too much make-up on the wrinkles around her eyes and small balloons of rouge on each cheek. It's her eyes, with their blue-greyness, that hold me, so intent on interpreting the broken smoke blankets straggling from the fire.

Her voice takes on an Irish lilt as she describes the farm in Galway where her father lived and in his mind all of the years he spent on Tyneside. She wears a starch-stiff pinny and slippers with half-a-fur halo that give her bunions comfort. She examines the fire as my breath stops. Lost in a mythical past, travelling to Ireland she never visited she begins to speak in a hushed voice. This was our secret. Granda was out. We are co-conspirators, 'There's money', she said and carefully felt the palms of her hands and added, 'Definitely'. I did not speak as she whispered, 'A pot of gold from America'.

Granda had a part-time job after retiring from working in the shipyards on the Tyne and now worked as a labourer in a bakery and from the little he said I gathered he burnt bread for whatever reason in a furnace that sometimes singed his eyebrows. There were always more questions than answers with Granda. He was not due home for an hour as me and Granny silently hunched by the fire.

You had to be careful with how much coal you placed on the fire. Too many coals dampened the flames that eventually sprung like a golden heart from the centre of the fire. Her belief she could read the smoke trails was undeniable. Had her mother or father given her this captivating skill? She was completely absorbed. I began to think she was some kind of mystic. I had no knowledge of those who said they were able to predict events and see the past and certainly the future so clearly. Granny was the first.

It was running into Christmas. Nights were cutting in. It was near-dark at four o'clock. The curtains were still open but lights in the house were all off. There was only the stuttering light from the coal fire settling through the room where Granny believed she could see the future.

In what seemed an age she had not really spoken, the odd word was all I had to hang onto like a desperate man about to fall from a ledge. I see wisps of smoke, even now, drifting leaf-like toward the black abyss of the chimney. Her eyes tightened at the knock on the door.

It was too early for Granda and it wasn't the rent collector's day. We sat open-mouthed; my mouth began to dry. Granny moved in tiny fearful steps. The knocking continued as she scattered toward the door. I stood perfectly still until I realised the fire was burning my leg.

She returned with a stranger; a man, dressed like the tailors' dummy in the outfitters that always had me amazed. It was her brother John from America. I was introduced. Granny cried happy tears. I stared at Granny, my belief in her mystic powers cemented forever.

• *Saturday Bet* •

I AM GOING BACK to the house I spent so many hours in. It is an easy journey. Eating chips bigger than I have ever seen. There is an egg on top of the chip mountain. It must be a Saturday. The Holy Ghost print, big as a poster for a rock concert, is sternly watching me. Maybe he wants my chips. The radio is on. The TV sits in the corner silently, the half-closed curtain casting a shadow over the screen. The television will spring into action when horse racing begins. Short trousers have my calf hairs standing to attention. I aim them toward the fire. Granda does not move. The fire is his. Granny hovers in the near-distance. She rarely sits. Her pinny slaps like a flag on a flag pole as she moves around the house.

Granda gives me his bet. He writes with a 'vine', his word for a pencil and writes so heavily it is almost embossed on a torn piece of paper. I have to go to Mr O'Neill's to place a bet that Granda wraps around the coins. Granny, at the last moment, gives me money to place an each-way bet on the tipster; *Templegate*.

The Betting Shop is a council house just around the corner from Granda and Granny's. I go to the back door passing their toilet and kitchen. Mr O'Neill's bald head glistens with a fine film of sweat as he prays to the bets and money spreading themselves on the table in front of him. He makes a note of everything. He does not look at me taking my bet. There are other people in his living room. The talk is of winners and losers. I pause until Mr O'Neill says, without looking at me, 'that's champion son'.

One day he would not take my bet. He just said, 'Tell ya Granda there's goin' to be aa raid.' He shoved the money and bet back into the palm of my hand. There was no one in his living room talking of horses. Granda looked at me. He waited for me to speak. I told him Mr O'Neill was by himself and was wearing a hat. Granda stopped me talking with two hands in front of my face. He just said, 'And?' 'Mr O'Neill took me to his gate and was with his dog. It's black and white and always barks at me.' Granda looked sternly at Granny. He didn't want to raise his voice. Granny said, 'What happened with the bet?' I put my hand in my jacket pocket and showed them the crumpled piece of paper and money. 'Mr O'Neill said, 'Tell ye Granda there is going to be another raid.' Granda took the money and bet and nodding grumpily said, 'I hope this lot don't win.' Granny walked over and put on the TV as Granda handed Granny her money for the bet that could not be placed. 'What happened?' I forget. The 'raid' would have been a visit by the police to try and stop illegal gambling. It didn't.

Weeks later I went to Mr O'Neill's. It was really busy. His dog eyed me from under the table but forgot to bark. Back in Granny and Granda's the TV was loud. Granda stared at the screen like a Chess

Grandmaster. He held the bet in his hand and as the afternoon wore on, gave Granny almost sly looks. Granny, for once, was oblivious of his apparent interest in her, she was looking out of the window and diving through the front door to talk to neighbours from a distance. Occasionally elderly friends would shuffle up the path, sharing gossip.

She would come back and tell of so-and-so's death or who was paid-off from his or her job. Granda barely raised a nod. The piece of paper in his hand seemed to become smaller. One bet ended-up in the fire. Still Granny was unaware of Granda's rising excitement.

'What happened?' Granda switched off the TV. Granny started to make the tea. It was mince-and-something. I watched her eyeing the frying pan as if it were the enemy. Cooking always baffled her. Granda was a better cook. He had been taught as a young man the mystery of cooking. Granny was hoping the water would turn to wine. It never did. She dropped the mince on the kitchen floor and scooped it up like a first-class cricket wicket-keeper. She turned to me at the door of the kitchen and put a finger to her lips. I got the message: say nowt.

There was a strange silence. No radio or TV. Granda was staring into the fire. He had not smoked his pipe. He put on his coat, struggled with his flat cap as if he was tightening a bolt on his recently hair-cut-head and left the house without a word spoken. Granny heard the door slam which broke through her deafness. She spun round as if she was going to attack me and shouted, which she rarely did, 'Has he gone out?' I had not seen Granny move so quickly, pushing the curtains open she always hid behind so she could see her neighbours. He had gone. I was left with Granny, who was nothing short of distraught. She sat in Granda's seat, something she never ever did, examining the fire, she believed in the power of reading the flames. After a short-eternity she spoke, 'There is money coming to us.' I was convinced she was right, especially after staring at me with real intensity. She switched on the TV and radio at the same time. The noise was terrible. I was sure next-door would be banging on the wall. She ran around the room, then swiftly upstairs. The regularity of her life had been thrown out of the window: Granda had left the house.

In the middle of this mayhem Granda returned. Switched off the TV and radio. A herd of elephants battered down the stairs and Granny dived into the living room as Granda stared at her for what appeared to be a life-time. Granda shouted, 'Your bet came up!' Placing the worn-out looking pound notes on the table beside three empty plates.

• *13 Days* •

—*The Cuban Missile Crisis lasted 13 days
from October 15 to 28, 1962.*

I AM FIFTEEN-AND-A HALF. The half must be important. See me hollow-cheeked with running most days. Soon I'll be watching the news which fills my dreams and every waking hour.

Here is more of the picture: dark hair swept over my brow, reminding me now of the shape of a sculler boat for some reason. I wear black-framed glasses from God-knows-where but some style consultant should buy themselves another pair of glasses when working on their next design. They do, however, allow me to see the number of a bus.

My track suit is black and the top has a big collar. My training shoes are heavy. It is a dark night in October, rain spittles on my glasses and has my world speckled which seems to appeal to me. We are on a six-mile run and are a strong pack. Running in unison: No one has dug their elbows into my ribs and nobody has verbal diarrhoea. I am happy with the rhythmic slapping of our trainers and silence cocoons me. We finish the run at the club's HQ. Over the last mile or so the pace really quickens up but we stay like a powerful adhesive together. Eventually we stand in a bedraggled circle for a few minutes and all forego the club's trickling water shower and head home for a bath.

Dad is in his early forties, I now calculate. He is a labourer in a factory. Factory work does not suit him. He feels too confined; something he has never said but I smell his entrapment day-in and day-out. He nods as I head to the cold bath where my stay is brief, somebody had forgotten to put on the boiler. Probably me.

It is a Thursday night and dad has a ten-bob note in his pocket and could go for a pint or three but he is still in his work clothes: a torn and sweaty shirt, trousers streaked with what looks like oil. I don't ask. The TV is on. My family must be there. I can see the screen with images of JFK and Khrushchev.

I do not recall any specific statements just dad's serious face. His eyes become pin points of anxiety and lips purse at each word. I examined him watching these two world leaders. He was angry and perplexed that this could happen again. Will there be a world war? After dad turned off the TV the picture disappeared like I imagined our world would go: quickly. Lost forever.

I AM MYOPIC. I had broken my glasses and needed to go for my first job interview. Not a good start. I thought, at sixteen, going on seventeen, meant I definitely could not go. My mother went apoplectic when I suggested I miss the interview, 'I had to.' I looked for comfort from Granny. She would realise I would feel very uncomfortable because of my poor eyesight and could not find my way there. Granny was incredulous. How could I think of not going? The die was cast.

After finding a compliant wall I made my way to the shipyard office where I had to be interviewed. Picture Blind Pew from *Treasure Island*. Now the interview, like my eyes, is not clear. The office, however, is printed strongly on my memory: I had slipped into a Dickens novel. Take away the harsh fluorescent lights on the ceiling and everything else was Bob Cratchit. I was surprised, initially, as to why the rest of the staff did not talk about Ebenezer Scrooge. Heavy jackets and the arses of trousers shining like a brand-new half-crown were the order of the day. Shirts and ties, not matching, completed the dress code. Ebenezer may not have approved.

Outside the office, boats were being repaired in the shipyard and the noise was unbelievable. Frightening. Caulkers' and riveters' hammers attacked the air and echoed around the docks. No one seemed to notice. This was my new normality. At dinner-time I walked round the shipyard. Can you see me? Black Donkey jacket and brightly coloured shirt with a tab collar. I still sense my insecurity.

'What did I do?' I worked in the Time-Office, I checked and calculated workers' time spent on their job. Have you noticed how people rarely ask what you do at work after you tell them you have an office job? Words like 'Accounts', and 'Wage Department' seem to suffice. Then you talk about getting to and from work. This is what I did in the Time-Office; I wrote in huge ledgers. How 'huge' is 'huge?' Spread both your arms out as far as they will stretch and about half that span is the width of the black ledgers. They are made of metal and you attach ledger sheets into punch holes. I hope the picture is clear.

I soon learnt some men were not always happy about how much they were being paid. Men, generally smelling of beer, would come to our window in the Time-Office and tell us that they wanted their pay sorted or they would 'sort us' out. I would dive to the office door and lock it quickly or if that failed hold my foot and the rest of my body against the bottom of the door. One man told me, several times, his wages were wrong. He refused to accept anything I said. I stood at a window where queries were dealt with. I eventually closed the window on this man as he had drunk so much it was difficult to understand anything he was trying to say. I brought the window down. And fastened the bolt that locked it. The next moment I was covered in glass. He had put his fist through the window. The police were called. The man stood in the yard, outside our office, telling of his complaints to anyone who would listen while blood dripped from his hand. The policeman asked if he had broken the window. He said, 'No'. He was then asked how he cut his hand. He said, 'Shaving this morning'.

Shaving did not feature with the Tank Cleaners. They had to get oil from the inside of tanks, going into the hold of a ship on make-shift ladders, after a pump had taken as much oil out of the tank as it possibly could. The oil had to be removed before the ship could leave the dock on the tide. These were mostly young men dressed in rags. No masks. No hard hats or breathing equipment. They had a lop-sided cabin where they kept haversacks with sandwiches that they would eat after their journey to the bowels of the hold. In the corner of the yard was a 45-gallon drum, filled with 'Swarfega', which helped clean oil from their arms and faces.

It is winter. I am with the Tank Cleaners' Foreman asking how many hours his men had worked during the night. The drum is covered with ice. A young lad, about the same age as me, picks up a metal bar and smashes the ice which is preventing him from getting at the 'Swarfega'. The noise is of a skull being smashed. The ice shatters across the drum as I take off my repaired broken glasses and place them in my inside jacket pocket and the young lad becomes a blur that is with me today.

• *Sorry* •

TREVOR WAS QUIET. That troubled me. His long fingers carefully held the pen as he wrote requests for housing repairs. A quietness stunned the office. I was young and had neither knowledge or confidence to break the silence. I stared at the walls; important messages were busy turning yellow. No one had bothered to take them down as if the past had to be there.

Trevor drew in his breath with a desperateness I found unsettling. I noticed, for the first time, his jacket was worn at the sleeves and provided a dark border for pasty-white bony hands. Did he know I was examining him? He said nothing as he searched under paperwork for reading glasses. The telephone ringing shocked me. I answered the call and was confronted by a shrill demanding voice. I had to do something quickly about a problem with their plumbing.

Trevor did not move as he wrote and wrote with such intensity it made me sweat. The office became smaller and I took off my jacket which was a newer version of Trevor's. Loud banging on the portacabin woke his nervousness and he stepped outside.

He returned and said nothing. The silence was oppressive and held me at my desk as I watched the traffic flow slowly by. I found myself writing more and more receipts and advice notes which began to cover my desk. He was working behind me. The door slammed. I turned and found an envelope addressed to me. He was standing outside the window and held a finger to his lips, wanting me to obey his silence.

I chose silence. He left and was soon in the distance. He did not look back. I placed the envelope in my inside pocket. It felt like a dead weight, heavy as his body which hung from a banister that night.

I was young. I did not know what to say. His note just said, 'sorry'.

THIS IS 1972. ME AND GRANDA are sitting by the coal fire. Granny is clumping above us before heading off to the shops. She shouted, 'I'll not be long.' Granda did not reply. I aped his silence. He sucked his pipe. The stem was bone white. His black boots stood guard by the side of the fireplace; they glowed, competing with the fire.

Picture me: side-burns; shirt with long pointed collars; Fair Isle jumper, like Paul McCartney, I thought. Corduroy trousers and Chelsea boots with elasticated sides crumpling tightly round my ankles complete this self-portrait.

We were both capable of holding silence. It seemed days could pass in these hold-your-breath moments. I had a newspaper article on the *Wellesley*. Granda's eyes were drawn to it but silence was still winning.

Leaving work and talking to Granda was all I intended to do. I had kept a sandwich from my dinner and ate it on the way to Granny and Granda's who had already eaten; their plates in the sink, dowsed in cold water, like tripe in a bucket.

'The *Wellesley* kept us fit. Plenty swimming. I could run up a tree. Not that there were any trees on the ship. I was always a good swimmer. I won a few races.' Granda had broken the silence. The *Wellesley* was a training ship on the Tyne for boys who were, 'waifs and strays.' Their words not mine.

His pipe indicated the photograph in the newspaper, 'I can see meself going over the same exercises time and time again.'

I had to ask him, 'How did you end-up there?' Questions, with Granda, were to be avoided; he expected a nod of acquiescence from me. For once he started to talk about his time on the ship, looking in the fire. He was not just lost in the past, he was there. The look in his eyes changed, they became bright, alert and dived around the flames as if he was searching for the lads that shared his life.

He spoke quickly, 'One of the lads was telling me he swam ashore. Stayed with a lass all night and did all sorts. So he said. Another lad told me, 'You can do that with boys.'

I said, 'What?'

'Go with a lad?' He replied.

I said, 'Kissing a lad? That'll never happen.'

Then he said, 'I've done it.' And went right up to me and whispered, 'Loads of times?' He talked about there being two hundred lads on the ship and you had to find love somewhere. He tried to kiss me and said, 'There are a few lads here that have kissing games.'

Stepping back, I said, 'That's not for me.' Then he tried to kiss me again.

I dived out the way. He cried and said, 'Will you still be my friend?' Looking at him I said, 'As long as you don't try that kissing carry-on.'

I could not believe me and Granda were having this conversation. Granda was dead old and had a short-back-and-sides haircut off Billy the Barber, who went from door-to-door butchering men's hair talking about horse-racing so quickly his words ran into each other and his false teeth clattered like plates falling on the stone kitchen floor.

I didn't know if I wanted to stay. Sweat tickled my arm-pits. I could not look at my crimson face in the distorted mirror above the fire place. I stared at the wall, hoping for salvation or at the very least Granda to start talking about anything but boys' kissing. This was not turning out the way I wanted. Although I did not know which way that was.

Silence was king again but somehow Granda was more relaxed as if we had bridged a gap and we would never be the same. He sucked harder on his pipe and let the smoke glide up the chimney. He continued his tale. Looking at him I thought his bulbous lips and squat nose suggested a heritage I could only guess at. Short grey hair matched his eyes. Now his hands were soft after years of retirement, no longer a rigger in the shipyards, making magic with rope and twine.

He drew in breath, sounding like cold wind coming around a corner. Yet there was no threat, it was more of a break in the tale I had been waiting so long to hear. 'I was a bastard', he said, and savoured the silence and impact upon me.

Never having heard Granda swear had me pursing my lips and loosening the top button on my shirt.

He was not waiting for a reply. The look on his face told me he was stepping into his past and there were steep steps where he could fall. I had never been here before: He was changing before my eyes. He said, slowly, 'Make a cup of tea.'

I watched the back of his head from the cold kitchen. He was immobile.

Two mugs were filled from the tea pot with a woolly blanket that was always hot. One sugar for Granda and none for me. I returned to him and felt he had hypnotised me and he was a Buddha in a Jarrow time-travelling-house. I needed the story to continue and for Granny not to return and break this spell. I wanted to hear more of his tale for the first time.

He began to speak again and his voice was different, so much younger. 'Aa saw him years later. The lad I was telling you about that liked kissing lads. He was getting knocked about and called names. I scattered them. He said, 'Thanks, and you know I have always loved you.' Then he cried and make-up ran down his cheeks. You know he just wanted a bit love. There were no love rations on the *Wellesley*.

The front door rattled open and Granny bustled into the living room. I looked at Granda as his body language changed, returning to the man I had become so used to. I finished my tea quickly, gave Granny a cuddle and without a backward glance shut the door on the usual silence.

· *Left Without Saying* ·

I AM IN THE LOUNGE of a new estate pub no longer there; the carpet is still thick and I can see my footprints as if in snow. Granda is in the bar by himself, smiling and that was never his style. He is wearing a navy-blue suit with the look of not being dry-cleaned in years, the collar turning up at the back. He will be 'counting coppas' in his pocket making sure he has enough money for his rent. I watch him circle the men standing at the bar. He is desperate for company: anyone to talk to. Do they know him? Is he an 'old nuisance?' Someone that is 'harmless'; these are expressions they may use.

I watch him intently. This is a snapshot. There is no punch-line. No one enters the bar and beats him up. Or buys him a pint as he tells them of his life leading to him standing alone. His smile stays fixed. What you have to know is that he was not 'big' on smiling and was not a great talker. Now it seems as if he wants to talk all night. Tell everyone who cares to listen. This was my opportunity to hear his story. Walk him home. Take off his jacket. Straighten his collar. Help him out of his boots. Shuffle him into bed or at least throw a blanket around him in front of the coal fire. I did nothing. I left Granda alone wanting to talk and that failure haunts me.

I cannot see him with Granny and me, a few years earlier, when she was lying on the settee in their living room, not wearing make-up which was rare. Gone is the rouge on cheeks, her face seems ill-defined and has a strange pallor that has my stomach in a knot with nerves bubbling. She wanted to die at home. Not in the hospital that used to be a Workhouse. 'Not there,' she said. Over and over.

I would love to say she lived longer and told me more stories and half-truths. She died within a few days of me kneeling by that settee with the world going on as usual. I was a pall-bearer at her funeral, with a glass of whiskey having me stumbling down their sharp wooden stairs.

Granda was on the horizon of my life for a year or so after seeing him in the pub. I visited him in hospital, stood at the end of his bed, his half-smile and near-silence still rings tinnitus-like and seems determined to stay. There was no secret letter from Granda and Granny buried in a drawer of their council house giving me answers to the questions filling my head now.

Is it unreasonable to want to know more of their lives? I never saw them write a letter. Why should I have expected one? Why feed on their silence that bled through their lives and now has become part of mine as I dwell on answers, I wanted them to give.

AS A BAIRN I WOULD PLAY at 'Jarra Slacks,' mud flats, near Saint Pauls' church at the mouth of the river Don. It was there I first heard stories of a man being hung and covered in pitch. That terrified me and filled many a nightmare. I see myself playing among the wooden crucifix-like remains of the walkways where timber was seasoned. Big lads are jumping from timber to timber and each time they land water runs right up to their faces. The water is too deep for me. I don't jump. I can't swim. And I'm dead scared. It's getting dark and I want to go home. My mother will come looking for me and I'll be embarrassed if she turns up shouting.

I start to edge away when one of the big lads shouts, 'Ye not going home?' I shook my head meekly as I put my shoes round my neck by tying the laces together. My socks were sticking out of my shoes like an inquisitive crumpled mouse. I began to wade towards the timbers where the big lads were. The water's tar black and scuttled rat-like into my underpants. The lads started to laugh at me. I did not want to go any further but decided going back was not an option. The water was up to my waist. As I looked at the lads standing on the timbers I walked quicker: it was now or never. The next moment sees me fighting for breath and breathing in black sludge. One of the lads grabbed my hair, dragging me to the bank. I threw up black vomit. He pulled up great clumps of grass to wipe my face and legs. The others did not seem to notice. I was pitch black and when I eventually got home my mother screamed and put me in the tin bath nowhere near the fire, without heating up the water. That must have been part of the punishment; Jobling's treatment was harsher.

It was in 1972, when I became immersed in William Jobling research for the exhibition, *The Gibbetting of Wm. Jobling* at the Bede Gallery, Jarrow, which was held in October that year. I wrote the chapbook which accompanied the exhibition. Prior to that the doyen of north-east writing, Sid Chaplin, had written an article for the Jarrow Festival programme in 1971 prompting Vincent Rea, curator of the Bede Gallery, to organise the Jobling exhibition which went on to successfully tour the U.K. That was all later.

I began to dream about Jobling, Hepburn the Pitman's leader and Jobling's wife Isabella, who lived in a cottage overlooking the Slake and near where I fell as a child. Researching Jobling took over me beginning with the book by Ellen Wilkinson, *The Town That was Murdered*, published in 1939 and revered in Jarrow. I discovered Professor Norman McCord of Newcastle University had written a paper in 1958 for the South Shields Archaeological and Historical Society, entitled, *The Murder of Nicholas Fairles, Esq., J.P., at Jarrow Slake, on June, 11, 1832*. Professor McCord kindly sent me a copy. That said the Jobling story had remained largely untold, although it features in Richard Fynes and A. M. Richardson's 'The Local Historian's Table Books.'

I went on to unearth Jobling's gibbet which was in Newcastle Keep. It had been given to the Newcastle Society of Antiquities in 1856 when Tyne Dock was developed. The gibbet was a key piece in the Bede Gallery exhibition.

The gibbet was a derrick, which would have been used to discharge cargo from ships on the Tyne. It originally extended to a height of twenty-one feet and was secured in a cement base in the Slaaks. We had the top eight feet, which can now be found in South Shields Museum. I helped to steer the gibbet out of the Keep as it raced down its stone steps. Our van dragged at the road leaving sparks flying: it was heavy.

Driving through Gateshead, on the way to the Bede Gallery, we passed Saint Mary's churchyard at Heworth where you will find a stone dedicated to those who lost their lives in the 1812 Felling Colliery disaster, including entire families from eight years of age. In that same cemetery lies the grave of Thomas Hepburn, who founded the Northern Union of Pitmen. His gravestone reads, 'This stone was erected by the miners of Northumberland and Durham and other friends.' It's the 'other friends' that has, for me, such power.

A cursory glance at colliery records reveals a frightening death toll. Jarrow's Pit was no exception: January 25th, 1817, forty-two men and boys were killed and in a near duplication of events in August 1830, a further forty-two lost their lives, leaving, on that occasion, twenty-one widows and sixty-six fatherless children.

From the beginning of the nineteenth century, miners had voiced their dissatisfaction with working conditions and their annual bonds and in 1810 they eventually went on strike. Mineworkers had to sign an annual contract known as a 'bond', which meant they were contracted to stay at a particular colliery for a year and a day. As most pitmen were illiterate, they would make their cross on the bond and the viewer or manager of the colliery would add the man's name.

The Northern Union of Pitmen of Tyne and Wear, led by Thomas Hepburn was established 1830. He was a Wesleyan Methodist, as were many pitmen, and lay preacher and learnt to read and write through classes organised by the Methodists.

In April, 1831, he led the pitmen on strike. He wanted boys to work only a twelve-hour day as they had been working sixteen hours. He also sought the abolition of the 'Tommy Shop' system. This was a system whereby pitmen were paid in 'Tommy checks,' vouchers, which could only be used in company stores at prices greatly unfavourable to them.

The strike led to battles between pitmen and the militia. Hepburn, at his meetings, pleaded with his men to keep a peaceful strike. Meetings were held at Black Fell, Boldon Colliery and Friars Goose, Gateshead and on one occasion, twenty thousand pitmen met on Newcastle's Town Moor. The strike lasted until September 1831. Some concessions were gained: Hepburn was made a full-time official but there was still bitter opposition to the union. In April 1832 there was another strike among pitmen when they refused to sign their annual bonds which led to violence and Cuthbert Skipsey, a miners' leader from North Shields was shot and killed by a 'special constable.' Incidentally Cuthbert was the poet Joseph Skipsey's father. The judge recommended leniency and the constable was given a six-month sentence with hard labour. 'Special constables' were essentially strike-breakers.

On June 11th 1832 at 5.00 p.m. Jarrow pitmen, Ralph Armstrong and William Jobling, were drinking in Turner's pub in South Shields, on the road, near the toll-bar gate, close to Jarrow Slake. Jobling begged from Nicholas Fairles, a 71-year-old well-known local magistrate. He refused. Armstrong, who had followed Jobling, attacked Fairles with a stick and a stone. Both men ran away leaving Fairles seriously injured on the road. Two hours later Jobling was arrested on South Shields beach where horse racing was taking place. Armstrong, an ex-seaman, apparently returned to sea and conjecture.

After his arrest Jobling was taken to Fairles home and identified as having been present but had not been the main assailant. Jobling was taken to Durham Jail and when Fairles died of his injuries on June 21st, he was charged with murder. Jobling was tried at Durham Assizes on Wednesday, August 1st. The jury took fifteen minutes in reaching their guilty verdict.

Judge Parke, in his summing-up attacked the unions, 'Combinations which are alike injurious to the public interest and to the interests of those persons concerned in them...I trust that death will deter them following your example'. The sentence was that Jobling be publicly executed and his body be hung from a gibbet erected in Jarrow Slake, near the scene of the attack. The judge continued, 'I trust that the sight of that will have some affect upon those, who are to a certain extent, your companions in guilt and your companions in these *illegal proceedings*, which have disgraced the county. May they take warning by your fate'. Jobling was the last man gibbeted in the North.

Jobling was hung on August 3rd. Hepburn asked his men not to attend the hanging to avoid clashes with the militia and held a meeting on Boldon Fell. After Jobling was taken from the scaffold, his clothes were removed and body covered in pitch. He was then riveted into an iron cage, made of flat iron bars two and a half inches wide. His feet were placed in stirrups from which bars of iron went each side of his head and ended in a ring, which suspended his cage. Jobling's hands hung by his sides, and his head was covered with a white cloth. In a four-wheeled wagon, drawn by two horses, on Monday, August 6th, he was taken to Jarrow Slake escorted by a troop of Hussars and two companies of Infantry.

The gibbet was fixed upon a stone weighing one and half tons and sunk into the Slake; the heavy wooden uprights were reinforced with steel bars to prevent it being sawn through. At high tide the water covered four to five feet of the gibbet leaving a further sixteen to seventeen feet visible. Isabella, Jobling's wife, had a cottage near the Slake and would have been able to see her husband clearly for the three weeks he was displayed. On August 31st, when the guard was removed, Jobling's friends, risking seven years transportation, stole the body. Attempts have been made to discover Jobling's body but to no avail.

By September 1832, the strike had petered out; the union was almost non-existent not reviving for a number of years. The annual bonds were not abolished until some forty years later. When the union died, Hepburn tried to sell tea from door-to-door, but anyone buying from him risked losing their job.

Eventually, starving, Hepburn went to Felling Colliery and asked for work. He was offered employment provided he had no further dealings with the union. He conformed and devoted the remainder of his life to educating pitmen and became involved with the Chartist movement. In April 1891 Isabella Jobling went into South Shields Work House, and died there, too senile to recall her husband. Jarrow's colliery closed in 1852 and now there is no indication of where it stood, a school can be found near its former site. Much of Jarrow's Slake has been reclaimed.

I am not defending Jobling's involvement in the killing of Nicholas Fairles, a 71-year-old man; he was an accomplice to the murder, carried out by Ralph Armstrong. Armstrong was never apprehended. It is what the authorities did with Jobling's body and why which particularly hurts me.

What effect did Jobling have? What power did the cage swinging on Jarrow slake evoke? It is a powerful image that was with me as a child over a hundred and twenty years later. It underlined the ruthlessness of the government of the day. Were the pitmen of Tyne and Wear bowed by its power? Perhaps the French Revolution was too near and it was felt the working class should be treated harshly at any sign of insurrection. I suggest Judge Parke, the judge at Jobling's trial and the Home Secretary, Lord Melbourne, made Jobling a symbol, a battering ram, butting the pitmen of 1832 back to work to break the union. It had the desired effect.

What would have happened if the unions had become successful and a working-class revolt had become a reality? And if there had been a more cohesive and organised revolt on a national scale? If Jobling, the Peterloo massacre of 1819 and other attempts at working class rebellion, during this period, had brought about change? Shelley, after the

Peterloo massacre, asked we use this bludgeoning
as a means of change:

> Shake your chains to earth like dew
> Which in sleep had fallen on you—
> Ye are many—they are few.

• *Ellen, Maggie and Me* •

I AM LOOKING AT a photograph from 1933 of Palmers, the great Jarrow shipyard on Tyneside. It had just closed, making most of the town unemployed. My Granny, Maggie, was trying to make ends meet and failing. The Thirties are hard and it's going to get harder and she knew that better than me. She never did leave me any notes so I decided to write-up what she had told me over the years. And the past began to appear 'clear as day,' which was one of her expressions.

Jarrow's MP from 1935 was Ellen Wilkinson. This is the way I would love to believe she would have felt: 'My first time in Jarrow. I had seen poverty but not this defeat in people: it made me ill. My heart was wrung out. I saw knots of worn-out men hanging round corners, lined faces told their stories: hunger, cramped lives, hearts and heads held in a giant vice, locked in pain. I looked again at these old men and women and they were young and trapped. The government had closed ranks on them. Later they decided, in the words of the President of the Board of Trade, Lord Runciman, that Jarrow 'must work out its own salvation.' I was hungry to change their lives. I held a meeting on the Pit Heap at Jarrow and saw men's eyes glisten in the blue-black-gas-lamped night and was lifted, guided by their pain. The government has closed its all-seeing eyes and decided not to witness the devastation it was causing. An entire town does not deserve to live like this.

I could hear the emotion in my voice and held-in rage as I spoke, 'I will do my utmost. You will be my witness, if I fail you must tell me. My failure must not happen. Let's reach for the stars....' After the meeting I talked to families and they revealed the harsh realities of their lives. The child mortality rate was eleven percent. These were not mere statistics. Their demands for the bare necessities were being denied. I had a burning hatred for all in power, but I knew I could not allow that to rule.'

In the 1930s marching, as a means of protest, was not unusual. The blind marched from Edinburgh and miners from Wales, all saying the same thing: what is happening can only be wrong. Jarrow Council organised a march to London in October 1936. Maggie was at Ellen's meeting. She told me in the mid-1960s but the memory of that was still fresh. Granda had a part-time job after leaving the shipyards. She had time to tell her tale.

'I was on the Pit Heap. There were hundreds there. When Ellen got up to speak, with her red hair, that's just one of the reasons she was called, "Red Ellen."

It was her politics. Aa'll never forget it. Aa was lifted. Aa thought she can do something; we can escape this. You know we had nowt. TB in Jarrow was aa scourge. Aa was hungry all the time. The walls in our homes were filled with beetles, we called them 'bugs', we would squash and see blood splashing

78

on the walls. We felt our blood was being taken and wasted. Our lives were aa wash-out. I lost two bairns at birth.

Do you know hunger? You think of nowt else. Don't talk to me of problems, until you've known real poverty. On the night of Ellen's meeting, stars seemed to be sitting on me head, the air had aa bite but it was fresh, it smelt of hope. She gave me a sprig of hope, something aa'd never known. Never. I breathed something new, it made me forget about me empty belly.'

Ellen suffered from asthma. Medication's more sophisticated now. At the time they thought it was psychosomatic. She used tablets. There were doubts about her cause of death. She was only fifty-six, and was the Minister of Education. Some intimated she committed suicide. Ellen was a passionate woman and has stayed in people's hearts and minds for over eighty years. Here is a photograph, of Ellen in full-flow. She was not some bloodless, passionless facsimile but the real bloody thing. This is a Jarrow Crusade photograph. Do you know who has the copyright on the photos? The Getty Foundation. The irony is not lost on me. In this photo Ellen's leading the march. She didn't walk all the way from Jarrow to London. She joined the march when she could leave Parliament. Here she is having a break with the marchers. It wasn't just a photo opportunity. This was the crusade to save a town. And what happened? Defeat's a bitter pill, it's hard to swallow.

Their petition was 'presented' to Parliament and that was it. No debate. Some of the marchers were all for going back into the House, causing a disturbance but that would have been undemocratic and Ellen persuaded them not to. What did the marchers achieve? What were they given? Second-hand suits and third-class rail ticket back to Jarrow.

What saved Jarrow? Some would say the Second World War. Maggie worked in the shipyard during the war and bloody loved it. She had independence and a wage packet. Here she is. I hear her voice clear as any bell.

'Aa got aa job as aa Lady Driller during the war. It was bloody hard. When aa first started aa couldn't lift the drill, men would stand around, watching me struggle, laughing their socks off. By the end aa could throw it over me shoulder as if it was aa bairn. They stopped laughing. Mind you've got to be careful when the drill bits snaps, they fly all over the place. One flew off and hit the foreman right up the arse! All the lasses laughed but he never said aa word. Just walked slowly to the lavatory, where he screamed like aa stuffed pig.

I'm expecting; aa pray it's a boy. That's what me man wants. Not that he has ever said. He did say the marchers had been sold down the river. He used to get really mad but he was never good with words. He would just stand in the backyard. I knew to leave him alone. Mind he thought the world of Ellen.'

I picture Ellen alone, after the marchers have had their boat trip on the Thames, after they have picked-up their second-hand suits and after waving off the marchers at King's Cross. Do you know that feeling? Not just lasting for few days, dragging its heels through your heart and soul until you have to do something to avoid the life you might end up with: and you know you have to make a change.

Ellen and Maggie's lives made me look at my life. I was reminded of what Maggie said, 'Me father could neither read nor write.' I am writing this for Ellen, Maggie and me.

Acknowledgements

These stories have appeared in the following publications and plays, sometimes in different versions. I would like to thank the magazine editors and producers of the plays for promoting my work.

1. 'Welcome Stranger' *Fragmented Voices* heart/h Anthology, October 2021; https://fragmentedvoices. com/product/heart-h-paperback/

2. 'Christmas Eve' *Fragmented Voices* published in September, 2020.
https://fragmentedvoices.com/2020/09/23/christmas-eve-hope-street-jarrow-by-tom-kelly/

3. 'Swim Out of Me dream' featured in *Drey* magazine number Four, Spring 2012. This is me as a child in Jarrow. Snots an all.

4. 'Confession' sees me at Saint Bede's Church, Jarrow.

5. 'The Day Rationing Ended' after fourteen years, at midnight on Sunday July 4th 1954. *The Crazy Oik*, Issue 52, Winter 2022; http://www.crazyoik.co.uk/issue52. htm

6. 'John Wayne and Me' began as a short story, then was a play, staged at the Customs House, South Shields in 2002 and here is a review of the production: https:// www.britishtheatreguide.info/reviews/secrets-rev.
It returned to its initial home as a short story in

December 2020 in the magazine *Cabinet Of Heed* https://cabinetofheed.com/2020/12/19/john-wayne-me-tom-kelly/

7. 'The Hen Cree', as a fledging short story, was first published in *Here Now* (3/4 1973/4), then developed into a play which you can find at Dramascripts. Granda and Granny leave their home of 48, Stanhope Road, Jarrow together: a rare event; www.dramascripts.co.uk

8. 'Seeing the Light' was in the *Fragmented Voices* 'heart/h' anthology, October, 2021; https://fragmentedvoices.com/product/heart-h-paperback/

9. 'At Eleven': I am the altar boy wearing a cassock and cotta and you can find this in the *Mono* magazine blog, August 2021 'At Eleven' by Tom Kelly (monofiction.org)

10. 'The Ironed Man' was published on The Penniless Press Website and in *The Crazy Oik,* Issue 46, Summer 2020; http://www.crazyoik.co.uk/issue46.htm

11. 'Pot of Gold'. Granny's life was one long belief that things will be better tomorrow. She had a lifetime of tomorrows. This story appeared in *Runcible Spoon,* May 2021; https://www.runciblespoon.co.uk/a-pot-of-gold/4595276017

12. 'Saturday Bet'. Published in *The Crazy Oik*, Issue 47, Autumn 2020; *http://www.crazyoik.co.uk/issue47.htm*

Illegal betting in Jarrow and everywhere else lasted until May 1961 when betting shops became legal.

13. '13 Days' was published in *Flash Fiction North* August 2020; https://www.flashfictionnorth.com/thepoetspage. I believed there was going to be a nuclear war. Bob Dylan's response, as we well know, was, 'A Hard Rain's A-Gonna Fall.'

14. 'Broken Glasses' appeared in *Fragmented Voices* February, 2021, and here I am working at the Mercantile Dry Docks, Jarrow. https://fragmentedvoices.com/2021/02/05/broken-glasses-by-tom-kelly/

15. 'Sorry': *The recusant*. Published June 2/2020; http://www.therecusant.org.uk/tom-kelly-prose/4594956927

16. 'No Love Rations' can be found in *Postbox,* Issue 4 (Postbox Press) November, 2020; https://www.redsquirrelpress.com/product-page/postbox.
The short story morphed into a one-man play, 'No Love Rations On The *Wellesley*, produced by Theatre N16 in August 2021.Here is the review: https://www.britishtheatreguide.info/reviews/coast-laurels-theatre-20126. My Granda was on the *Wellesley*, a training ship for 'waifs and strays' which was moored on the Tyne, off North Shields.

17. 'Left Without Saying'. This remembrance of Granda has eaten its way through me. Published in *The Crazy Oik*, Issue 49, Spring 2021; http://www.crazyoik.co.uk/issue49.htm

18. 'The Jobling Story' *Fragmented Voices,* April, 2021; https://fragmentedvoices.com/2021/04/09/the-gibetting-of-william-jobling-by-tom-kelly/

Here is a Jobling image from the touring exhibition when at the Bluecoat Gallery, Liverpool; https://my-bluecoat.org.uk/archive/bluecoat_arts/publications/posters/poster-for-exhibition-the-gibbeting-of-wm-jobling/

'The Town That Was Murdered,' written by Ellen Wilkinson with an introduction by Matt Perry (2019); https://bookmarksbookshop.co.uk/view/48879/The+Town+that+Was+Murdered

19. 'Ellen, Maggie and Me'. *Fragmented Voices,* November 27,2020; https://fragmentedvoices.com/2020/11/27/ellen-maggie-and-i-by-tom-kelly/

*

With thanks to Sheila Wakefield, Founder Editor of Red Squirrel Press for her continued encouragement and support, it is, as ever, really very much appreciated.

And my family, Linda, Bethan, Steve, Sophia, Vincent, Fiona, Paul, Aidan, Adam and Rachel with all my love.